Children of the
SEED GATHERERS

By Mary M. Worthylake

Illustrations by Henry Luhrs

MELMONT PUBLISHERS, INC., Chicago

Library of Congress Catalog Card Number:64-11115

© 1964, Melmont Publishers, Inc.

Printed in the U.S.A.

2 3 4 5 6 7 8 9 10 11 12   R   75 74 73 72 71 70 69 68

TABLE OF CONTENTS

FOREWORD

The Indians who once lived in the great central valleys of California and Oregon depended upon acorns for their chief source of food. Although there were many different tribes, their cultures were similar. Acorns were pounded in mortars. Acorn mush was cooked in water-tight baskets. Pottery was not used by these people, but they were the continent's finest basket-makers, particularly the Pomo women of Lake County, California.

In areas along coastal rivers, salmon and other fish were added to the diet. In the Klamath Lake region wild rice and wokas (seeds of the water lily) also provided food. The women dug roots and bulbs during the summer. Because of this they were often called "Digger" Indians. They gathered ripened grass seeds, nuts, and many kinds of berries. In the summer months

they wandered across the valleys and into the foothills harvesting roots and berries.

Tribes often came together to trade, exchanging their goods for things of other regions. The Pomo Indians made shell money which was used for trade. They also made lovely magnesite beads which were prized all up and down the coast.

Pomo houses were circular and were not excavated, as were the houses of most Indian tribes to the North. However, the sweat house—which was a part of every village—was partly underground.

A boy might have more than one name during his life time. A new name was usually given to him when he had killed his first deer.

Kiho and Lema in this story have followed the pattern of the Pomo Indians. But their way of life was characteristic of most acorn gatherers.

GATHERING ACORNS

Kiho woke early one morning in the moon of ripe acorns. He sat up on the sleeping bench and threw off his cover of deerskin.

Quickly he fastened his breech cloth around him. Bending low, he went through the door of the lodge.

A river ran in front of the lodge. Kiho jumped in the cool water and bathed quickly.

The sun was shining, making patches of light and shade in the meadow around the oak trees. The round houses of the village shone gold where the sun touched them.

The houses looked like big baskets turned upside down. They had been made by sticking poles in the ground in the form of a circle. The tops of the poles were bent together and tied with strong vines. Bunches of long grass or reeds were tied to the frame of the house and held in place with poles.

From a hole in the top of the lodge, smoke came out. Kiho's mother was cooking the morning meal and Kiho was hungry. He hurried to the house.

Tolo, his father, was already sitting on a mat beside the cooking fire. Kiho sat down beside him.

His mother, Yana, brought a basket of acorn mush for them to eat. Kiho dipped his fingers into the mush and then licked them. As he ate he watched his mother cooking more mush for the women, who would eat after he and his father were finished.

She picked up a hot rock between two sticks and dropped it into a basket. The hot rock made the water boil in the basket. Yana stirred the mush with a long wooden paddle.

"The acorns are almost all gone," Yana said. "We must gather more now and fill the storehouses."

Kiho looked at his father. The boy hoped that this year he would not have to pick up acorns. That was woman's work. But his father did not say a word.

When the women had finished eating, Yana took a big basket. She put it on her back and held it with a cord around her forehead. Kiho's little sister, Lema, also had a basket on her back.

"Come, son," Yana called to Kiho.

The boy picked up a basket and followed his mother. He knew that boys and girls must obey their parents. But he was glad to see that some of the other boys were also going to pick up acorns.

All day the women and children moved slowly across the valley beyond the river, from one huge oak tree to another. Kiho often climbed into a tree and shook the branches to make the acorns fall. This was more fun than bending over to pick up acorns.

All day the women and children gathered acorns. The next day, and for many days after that, they picked until their backs were tired.

The women made storehouses to hold the acorns.
Yana's storehouse had four tall poles set in a square.
A large rock in the middle of the square held up the
floor of the storehouse and kept the acorns off the damp
ground. The sides were woven like a basket. The woven
branches were tied with strong vines. The huge basket
was lined with pine needles and wormwood. Insects
and wood rats did not like the taste of these and would
not eat the acorns.

"Mother's storehouse looks like a big bird nest," Lema
said.

At last it was filled with acorns. Another was made
near it and was filled also. More acorns were buried
in the soft mud beside the spring where the village
got drinking water. These acorns would swell up and
after some months they would be sweet.

"Now we have enough acorns for the cold moons," Yana said. "We also have acorns to trade with people from the coast."

All winter she would shell acorns and pound them in a stone mortar. She pounded with a round stone which fitted her hand. Sometimes Yana went with other women to a big rock beside the river. There were many mortar holes in this rock. On warm, sunny days the women sat around the rock, pounding acorns. They liked to work together. They talked and sang.

The acorn meal was bitter. Yana took the bitter taste away by soaking the meal in warm water. She made a hole in the sand of the river bank and lined it with leaves. She put the meal in the hole and poured water over it. The water soaked away. Sometimes she poured water over the meal six or seven times before it was sweet.

Mush was made from the acorn meal. It was boiled in tight baskets which would hold water. Hot rocks made the water boil.

Sometimes Yana made acorn cakes and baked them in an oven of hot rocks. Sometimes she baked the cakes in a hole in the ground. The hole was lined with hot stones.

Acorns made the bread which the Indians ate, and acorn mush was their morning meal.

"I am glad many oak trees grow in our land," Kiho thought, "but next year I will surely be big enough so that I will not have to gather acorns!"

MAKING MONEY

"Our storehouses are full of acorns," Yana said one morning. "It is time for the people to leave the village and gather other foods."

Kiho and Lema liked the time of the year when they did not live in houses. They liked to move about over the Pomo land. They liked to sleep out of doors under brush shelters.

"Before we go we must make some new money," Tolo said. "My son, you can help me. We will need the money to trade with other tribes we will meet."

Kiho liked the times when friends got together at the berry patches. He liked to watch the men and women trading for things they needed.

He liked to do man's work with his father, too. But he did not like to make shell beads. That was hard work.

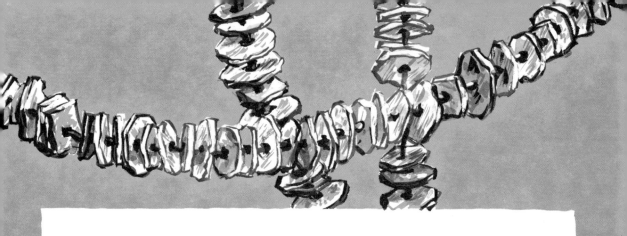

The shells were broken in little pieces. Then they were rubbed against a rough stone until they were smooth. Some pieces were round. Some were square. The hard part was making a hole in the shell. A stone with a sharp point was turned round and round. It was held against the shell. At last it made a hole in the shell. Then a string could be put through the shell.

The Pomo Indians were rich. They had many strings of shell beads. Other Indians wanted these beads. They would give nuts and paint and many other things for the beads.

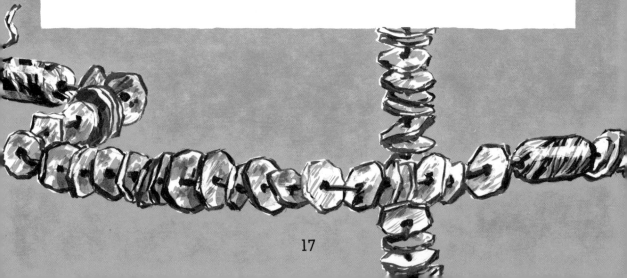

"When you go to the coast to get shells next time I would like to go with you," Kiho said.

"It is a long walk down the river to the beach," Tolo told the boy. "But I want you to learn how to choose the shells we need. I will take you when I go again."

Kiho's uncle came up, carrying a net full of stones.

"I have been to the white hills where we get the stone for beads," he told them. "Now we can make stone beads to use in trade."

The stone was easier to chip than the shells. But it was hard to make the beads all the same shape and to rub them until they were smooth.

"They are not pretty when we are making them," Kiho said. "But when they have been put in the fire they turn red and pink."

"People from other tribes like our beads," Tolo told his son. "They will give us many things in trade for them."

At the end of the day Kiho was glad to see the strings of beads his father would take to trade. But his hands were tired from turning the stone to make holes in the beads.

"Making money is hard work," he thought.

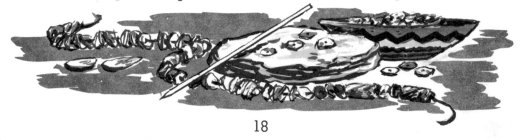

GATHERING FOOD

Kiho and Lema each carried a basket as they moved across the meadows with the people from the village. The women dug roots with long curved sticks. They put the roots in their big baskets. They beat seeds from the wild grasses which grew in the meadows.

For many days they camped beside a big lake. The men fished with nets in the lake. The women dried the fish. They gathered seeds and berries which grew beside the lake. They pulled the reeds, or tules, which grew at the water's edge. The reeds would make baskets and mats.

Kiho found the four poles which had held up a brush cover for them the year before. He and Lema gathered reeds and long grass to make another roof. His mother cooked beside this shelter. When the sun was hot they all sat in its shade, and at night they slept beneath it.

When they left the lake they climbed into the hills to gather berries which were ripe on the slopes. They met other tribes of Indians at the berry patches, some from the hot valley and some from the thick forests near the coast.

Everyone liked dried berries to eat in the winter. The berries were good mixed with the acorn mush. They were baked with roots. They were mixed with dried

salmon. Sometimes they were cooked in cakes with dried grasshoppers.

The women and children had baskets on their backs. As they picked they tossed the berries over their shoulders into the baskets.

The berries were spread out to dry in the hot sun. Some of them were put on a big slab of bark. A fire was built under the bark and the berries dried on the hot bark.

Lema felt very grown-up this year because she had a basket of her own. She was helping to pick berries.

"Do not get out of sight," her mother said. "The bushes are high above your head. A little girl can get lost in them."

Lema meant to mind, but she was very busy picking the berries. She saw a big clump of bushes where berries were thick. Lema picked fast. She tossed the berries over her shoulder into the basket.

Suddenly she heard a rustling noise on the other side of the berry patch.

"That must be Kiho," she thought. "He is trying to surprise me. I'll surprise him first."

She slipped quietly around the bushes and then she stopped, very frightened. A black bear was shaking the bushes with his paws. He was gobbling up the berries which fell to the ground.

Lema backed away, careful not to make any noise. She looked around wildly. Her mother was not in sight.

When she was a few feet away from the bear the little girl turned and ran as fast as she could. She did not look to see which way she was going. Her breath came fast and her heart was pounding. She thought the bear was right behind her. Then she tripped over a root and fell, with her berries rolling out of the basket all around her.

Something grabbed her from behind. She was sure it was the bear.

"Oh—oo-oo!" she howled.

"What is this?" cried a man, and Lema saw that it was her uncle. "Where are you going in such a hurry, little one?"

"A bear—a big bear—" she panted, pointing behind her.

"Where?" her uncle was excited. He picked up his bow and quiver of arrows from the ground.

Quietly he moved away. Lema saw him slipping around the clump of bushes. She saw him lift the bow and fit an arrow to it.

Zing! went the arrow. Zing! went another arrow.

"Come!" called her uncle. "Here is your berryeater. Tonight we will eat bear meat. It will be sweet because this bear has been eating berries. Your mother can tan this hide for your very own. On cold winter nights it will keep you warm."

Lema was careful to stay close to her mother after that. She stopped picking berries every few minutes to see if Yana was still near her.

But Kiho wished that he had been the one to see the bear. He was sure that he could have killed it.

TRADING

When berry picking in the hills was over, all of the Indians came together for a few days of trading.

People from the eastern mountains had brought big chunks of black, glassy rock. This was obsidian. It was used for making arrow heads.

People from the big rivers brought dried salmon. Others had dried deer meat and tanned deer skins.

The women in Kiho's village had many beautiful baskets to trade. They also had acorns which they gave for wild rice and for the pinon nuts which grew in the high eastern hills. The men used the shell money and the pink and red beads in trading.

Kiho wished that he had something to trade. He was glad when he saw his grandfather carrying a piece of obsidian. Now there would be new arrowheads.

When the trading was over the carrying nets and baskets were heavy.

It was time to go back to the village for the winter. Soon there would be rainy days and the brush shelters would not be warm or dry.

As Kiho's people moved back toward the village they gathered up the nuts and bulbs and roots which they had left in special places. At the lake they caught more fish to take with them. The loads on their backs were heavy. But there was much food for the rainy months.

Fresh grass and mats were tied to the outside of the lodge to keep out winter winds and rain. The food was stored in big baskets.

It was now time for the children to have lessons from their grandparents.

LEMA MAKES A BASKET

Lema's mother was too busy with gathering and preparing food to teach her little daughter to make baskets. So Lema learned from her grandmother.

"We have so many kinds of baskets!" Lema said. "Big, open ones to carry acorns. Baskets for gathering and baskets for storing. Tight ones to cook our acorn mush. Baskets with pretty patterns to wear on our heads. Little ones. Big ones. Even the baby sleeps in a woven cradle basket."

"You must learn to make all of these baskets," her grandmother told her. "Weaving is an important part of a woman's life. You can not keep house without many baskets."

Lema's first basket was of willow. Her grandmother showed her how to make coils for the bottom. She learned to weave in the filling around the heavier twigs.

When it was finished one side of the basket was taller than the other. The weaving was not straight.

Lema almost cried when she held the basket up for her grandmother to see.

"It is not good," she said sadly. "I can never make a pretty basket like yours."

"Not at first," agreed her grandmother. "It takes many years of practice. But you have made a start. Your next one will be better, and the one after that better yet."

Lema went with her mother to gather willow shoots, tule roots, ferns, grasses, cattail reeds, and many other materials for baskets. Some were peeled and soaked in cold water. Some were boiled in hot water. Some roots and buds were used for dye to make colored strips. These were woven to make pretty patterns.

"Before you begin a basket, you must think out the pattern in your head," Lema's grandmother said. "You must see a picture of it in your mind so you can make it the way you want it."

POMO CRADLE

28

The old woman's baskets were beautiful. Her cooking baskets were woven so tightly they held water. Some baskets were trimmed with feathers, red feathers from a woodpecker's head and black feathers from a quail's head.

Lema began another basket.

"I will teach my hands to work," she said. "Someday my baskets will be beautiful too."

The little girl also learned to make mats. The mats were made from the cattails, or rushes, which grew by the river. They were used on the floor. They were used also on the walls of the lodge.

When she was not weaving baskets, Lema went with her mother to gather many kinds of food—seeds, nuts, roots, and berries. She watched to learn how they were cooked.

"You are learning to do a woman's work," her mother told her.

A SICK BOY

One morning Kiho woke with a big pain in his stomach. He was sick. He put his hands on his stomach and groaned.

"The medicine man must come," Yana said.

Kiho was afraid of the medicine man. He wished he could hide.

The medicine man's face was painted with streaks of bright color. He wore a wide headdress of woodpecker feathers. In one hand he carried a rattle. In the other hand was a tube with feathers hanging from it.

Kiho's grandfather and some other men came into the lodge behind the medicine man. They sat down and began to sing. They kept time with split sticks which they slapped against their hands.

The medicine man danced around and around in the lodge. Sometimes he bent over Kiho and put the tube against the boy's stomach. He sucked on the tube. He was trying to draw out that bad thing which was making Kiho's stomach hurt.

The old men sang faster and faster. Their song pounded in Kiho's ears. The medicine man jumped about the room.

Suddenly he bent down and placed the tube on Kiho's lips. He sucked hard. Then he leaped back and put his hands over the end of the tube. He ran out of the lodge to the river. He seemed to throw something out into the river.

"Ah! Ah!" cried all the old men. "The medicine man has pulled out the pain. Now the boy will be well."

Kiho was taken to the sweat house. This was near the bank of the river. Kiho went down a ladder into the little room which was partly under the ground. A skin was hung over the door. It was dark inside the sweat house. No fresh air came in because the roof was covered with earth to keep the heat in.

A fire was built in the firehole and Kiho sat down beside it. Smoke went round and round in the room and the boy's eyes hurt.

Sweat covered Kiho's body. He rubbed himself with his hands. The sweat would help drive out the hurt in his stomach, too. More and more sweat covered him. He hardly could breathe in the hot, steamy air.

"Come out now," called the medicine man. "Run and jump in the river."

Kiho shivered when his hot body went under the cold water of the river. He picked up sand in his hands and scrubbed himself, trying to get warm again. Soon he came out of the water and fastened his deerskin belt around his waist.

"Now you will be well," said the medicine man.

Kiho found that his stomach pain was gone.

Tolo, his father, gave the medicine man a tanned buckskin robe to pay for making Kiho well.

KIHO SEEKS HIS POWER SPIRIT

Kiho's grandfather came to him one afternoon.

"You must go out to seek your spirit helper," the old man said. "Every hunter has to find a spirit which will help him all his life."

"What do I have to do?" asked Kiho.

"You must go up on a hill and stay all night by yourself. You must not drink any water, and you must not eat. If you sleep you may dream a good dream. The dream may have good medicine in it for you."

Kiho was glad that the time had come for him to look for his spirit. He knew he could not be a good hunter or fisherman unless he had a good spirit to help him. He did not want to be a medicine man—a shaman. But he did want to kill deer and catch fish. He wanted a good spirit to bring him good luck.

Yana smiled at her son. She did not like to think that he was going out all alone to be gone all night, but she wanted him to be a strong man. He was growing up. He must go alone.

Grandfather walked part of the way with him. They crossed the river at a shallow place and went under the oak trees across the flat. After an hour of walking they came to a hill.

"Go to the top of the hill," Grandfather said. "Make a little pile of stones there. Then fix a bed of branches or leaves. Lie there all night. Listen to all the sounds you hear. If you go to sleep remember what you dream."

The old man turned back toward the village.

Kiho climbed the hill. He piled up rocks to make a marker. He pulled weeds and grasses for a bed. He broke fir boughs and laid them on the bed. Then he sat down to watch the sun go out of sight. It was very quiet all around him. Never had he been so alone. But he was not afraid.

Daylight faded. The stars came out in the sky. A bird chirped sleepily in the tree behind him. A cricket chir-chirred beside his bed. A bird might bring a good spirit to help him. So might a cricket. But he had not gone to sleep yet. Perhaps he would have a dream.

Night noises kept him awake. He smelled the fir boughs under him. He looked up at the stars in the sky.

"I wonder what the stars are," he thought. "I see the road the ghosts take to the sky. Grandmother said the stars are flowers blooming in the sky. They do not look like flowers to me. They look like tiny suns and moons. Maybe the stars are the sun's children."

He looked for the Great Bear, and for the North Star, which his grandfather had said stood still in the sky. At night it would guide him if he were lost in the woods. The other stars moved in their places, but the North Star did not move.

Kiho fell asleep. When he opened his eyes he was cold and the sky in the east was turning pink.

"I did not have a dream," he thought sadly. "Perhaps I will not be a great hunter like my grandfather and my father. Perhaps I will have to stay with the women and pick berries and acorns all my life."

The boy started down the hill. Something moved below him. Grazing in plain sight was a huge elk. It raised its head. Kiho saw the elk's great, dark eyes. There was no fear in them.

Quietly he walked down the hill toward the elk. The big animal watched until the boy was almost at the foot of the hill. Then it gave a snort and walked away into the bushes, walking without hurrying.

Kiho looked after the elk. He had never seen one of the big animals so close before. Then he started toward the village. He met his grandfather coming for him.

"I did not have a dream, Grandfather," he said. "But I saw a big elk. He was not afraid of me. Could an elk be my spirit helper, do you think?"

"Yes, an elk spirit would be good," Grandfather said. "But you are young. You will come out again, and yet again, to sleep alone. If you dream of the elk or see it often you may be sure its spirit will guide you. Then there will always be meat in the village. You will grow to be a mighty hunter."

KIHO KILLS A DEER

"You must learn to shoot an arrow straight," Kiho's grandfather told him one morning. "I will help you make a bow and arrows."

They went into the woods. They hunted for the right kind of tree. With a bone knife the old man cut off a branch. For many days he worked with the wood, rubbing it with fat while it dried. He scraped it with a stone.

While the wood dried Kiho helped chip arrowheads. Most were of deer bones but some were of the glass-like obsidian. This rock made sharp arrowheads.

Kiho rubbed and polished the arrow shafts. He split the shaft and tied feathers on one end. On the other an arrowhead was tied.

"Watch where your arrows go," warned his grandfather. "Practice with the bone arrows. Save the sharp ones for real hunting. Always pick them up after you shoot. It is hard work to make them. Don't lose them."

When the bow was dry it was strung with deer sinews. Then Kiho practiced shooting every day. He and his friends learned to shoot straight. They learned to shoot fast.

One day his grandfather watched Kiho shoot. The old man smiled proudly when he saw that the boy

could hit the target almost every time.

"After this sleep we will go on a deer hunt," he said to Kiho. "We will see if you are a hunter."

Kiho was awake when dawn colored the sky. He quickly bathed in the river. He did not eat. One must not eat before a hunt.

His grandfather walked with him into the woods. The old man told Kiho what kind of bushes and grass the deer and elk liked to eat.

"They eat early in the morning and when the sun goes out of sight in the evening. The big bucks like to lie in the shade. They face into the wind so they can smell any danger which might come toward them. You must watch to see which way the wind is blowing. Come toward them up wind so they will not smell you."

Kiho listened carefully. He wanted to learn how to hunt. He put his feet where twigs would not crack and tell the deer he was coming. He sat quietly behind a bush at the edge of an open green meadow, waiting to see if a deer would come out to graze.

A doe and fawn came into the meadow. Kiho lifted his bow but his grandfather held his arm.

"Never kill the mothers or the young fawns unless you are starving," he said. "The fawns must grow until they are big and strong. The mothers must be left to have more fawns. Kill only a buck with antlers."

The old man and the boy walked to a small creek. They knelt to drink. Kiho saw tracks in the soft mud beside the water. They were sharp-toed tracks.

"A buck," Grandfather said. "A big one."

"The track is fresh, isn't it?" Kiho asked. "See, the water is just settling into it."

"Yes, the deer drank here just a little while ago. See if you can tell which way it went."

Quietly they walked into the forest. The old man stopped at the edge of a little mountain meadow. He sat down behind a clump of bushes. Kiho sat down beside him.

"We will wait here," the grandfather said. "Perhaps a deer will come out to feed. Sometimes we wear a deerskin and move as if we were feeding. Sometimes we rub sticks together to sound as if we were rubbing horns against a tree the way the bucks do in the fall. But today we will just sit quietly."

Kiho sat still. A blue jay scolded him. A squirrel saw him and scolded too. But after awhile the blue jay flew away. When the man and the boy did not move the squirrel stopped chattering and went on eating the seeds from a fir cone.

Kiho's legs hurt from sitting still. He moved and a twig cracked. His grandfather turned and looked at him and Kiho was sorry. He sat very still but he wished he had a deerskin to wear on his back. Then he could move about and pretend he was eating grass.

It seemed hours that he sat behind the bushes. Kiho was sure his legs would never wake up again. The woods were still and full of good smells.

Then his grandfather touched his arm. Kiho rose on his knees, slowly, very slowly, until he could see through the bushes. Grandfather was looking across the clearing. Kiho looked, too.

His breath came quickly. What he had thought were limbs on a manzanita bush were moving. A big buck stepped out into the meadow. His head was high. His antlers looked like branches as he walked into the clearing.

Grandfather made another motion. Carefully Kiho brought his bow up into position. Carefully he fitted a sharp-pointed arrow. Not even a twig stirred as he pulled back the bow string. The muscles of his brown arm swelled as he pulled with all his might.

Zing! The arrow shot through the air, straight toward the heart of the deer. The big buck leaped when the arrow hit him, and then fell to the ground.

Kiho had killed his first deer.

His grandfather showed him how to clean the deer and then the old man lifted it and carried it back to the village across his shoulders.

"We must have a feast!" Kiho's grandfather told the people in the village. "Our man child has killed his first deer. He has made his first journey to seek his spirit. He is now a young man. He must have a party!"

Kiho's mother and his grandmother cooked food. Lema helped. They roasted the deer meat. They made many cakes of ground acorn meal and of seeds and nuts.

At last everything was ready for the feast. All of the people in the village were invited. They all ate the good food which Kiho's family had prepared. They all ate but Kiho.

He could not eat any of the deer meat. If he ate the meat of his first deer he would never again be able to kill a deer. Never again would his arrow go straight.

Kiho ate an acorn meal cake and tried not to think about how good the deer meat must be.

When the feasting was over there were dances around the camp fires. The men danced hunting dances. They wore their headdresses of woodpecker quills and feathers. They wore strings of shell beads.

Kiho danced with the other boys, stamping his feet in time to the song. He wanted to learn the steps of the

dances. He wanted to take his place with the men of the village when they danced the old dances of their tribe.

Men kept time by clapping split sticks against their hands. One of them beat upon a hollow log. They sang as they clapped.

Kiho liked to listen to them sing. He knew they had learned the songs when they were boys as he was now. They were old, old songs. He must learn them too.

Then Kiho's grandfather stood up and began to talk.

"We have a feast tonight because one of our man-children has killed his first deer. It is time that he should have a grown-up name."

"Yes," said another old man. "He will soon be one of our hunters. He should have a new name."

"I will give him my father's name," Kiho's grandfather said. "That is a good name. When my father went to the spirit land we did not speak his name for a long time. Now we know he is happy in the spirit world. We can use his name again."

"That was a good name," agreed the other old men. "It will be a good name for this young hunter."

Now Kiho had a fine new name. It was a name which meant "Standing Elk." He was proud to have a grown-up name. He was proud to be one of the young hunters of the village.

Mary M. Worthylake was born in South Dakota but grew up on a Colorado homestead. Her parents moved to Oregon while she was still a teen-ager. Since then she has also lived in California, and Washington.

Mrs. Worthylake holds a B.A. and an M.Ed. degree from Western Washington College of Education, Bellingham, where she is a supervisor of student teachers. Her twenty or more years of professional experience have included teaching in both rural and city schools. Two of her most interesting positions were in a U.S. Navy dependents' school on Kwajalein, one of the Marshall Islands, and at the Lummi Day School on the Lummi Indian Reservation in Washington.

Mrs. Worthylake has written many children's stories and articles for periodicals. She is the mother of three children, has three step-children, and eighteen grandchildren.

Henry Luhrs, a Californian by birth, actually has not spent too much time in his native state. His work as a free lance illustrator has taken him both to New York and Chicago.

Mr. Luhrs' illustrations have appeared in such magazines as COSMOPOLITAN, COLLIERS, and RED BOOK. He has also illustrated a number of children's books for the Whitman Publishing Company as well as for Melmont.

Mr. Luhrs received his art training at the California Institute of Art in San Francisco as well as the Art League and Grand Central Art School in New York City. He and Mrs. Luhrs make their home in Laguna Beach, California.